CASTLE, ABBEY AND TOWN: HOW PEOPLE LIVED IN THE MIDDLE AGES

.

CASTLE, ABBEY AND TOWN

how people lived in the middle ages

by irma simonton black. illustrated
by w.t. mars. holiday house, new york

FOR JIM—
WITH LOVE AND THANKS
FOR HIS PARTICIPATION
IN THE STUDY THAT LED
TO THIS BOOK

CONTENTS

TO INTRODUCE THE MIDDLE AGES

THE EXCITEMENT of two knights charging pell-mell at each other in a tournament—that is one of the first things some people think of at the mention of the words "middle ages."

Tournaments were entertaining to participate in and to watch, but they had a more serious side. The knights were really practicing the art of battle. Medieval Europe was a warlike place, and at any time a knight might be called upon to fight.

Only strong knights ventured out on the open road by choice, for travel was hard and dangerous. The vast countryside, especially the dense forests, offered good hiding places to highwaymen and bandits. So most people stayed close to home, generally on the land where they had been born.

Since the distances from castle to castle were so great, each large estate had to be maintained separately, and the people

9

living there relied on each other. Everyone, from the lowliest serf to the lord of the castle, had his own duties. They welcomed exciting diversions like tournaments, gay hunts, or visits from minstrels. And they spent a lot of time in prayer, for their religious feeling was deep.

There was only one Christian church in those days and it was very strong. Monks, who dedicated their lives to God, put on somber robes and lived in peaceful monasteries. Here they tended gardens and went about a wide variety of spiritual and temporal duties.

Life on the great estates and in the monasteries went on as

it had for many centuries, but very gradually a few things began to change. By the end of the Middle Ages, a new and powerful middle class had appeared in the fast-growing towns: one example of the progress made toward modern times during this very important period.

The Middle Ages, then, was a time of excitement and danger, of isolation and self-reliance, of faith, progress, and much, much more.

The term refers to a period of about one thousand years following the collapse of the Roman Empire during the fifth century (400 to 500 A.D.). Modern historians divide this era

into the Early Middle Ages (until about 1050), the High Middle Ages (from 1050 to 1300), and finally the Late Middle Ages or Renaissance.

"Middle" was used because historians used to think of these years as a time of intellectual stagnation which came between the high civilizations of ancient Egypt, Greece and Rome, and modern times. More modern historians looked more closely into the period, however, and recognized it as a time of great and valuable change and growth.

What was life really like in those days? Clues come from fact and fiction, from artifacts and many other sources.

Stories about brave knights slaying fierce dragons, and beautiful princesses locked away in towers—these are fairy stories, but they originated in the Middle Ages, so they are full of the atmosphere of the period. Other stories are supposedly based on fact. In sixth century England, a real King Arthur probably met with his Knights of the Round Table. And there might have been a Robin Hood, or someone much like him, living in the twelfth century or later. Tales about them might have been the truth once, but they were told and retold so many times that the fact is hard to distinguish from the fiction.

Fortunately, there is also some historical fact to shed some light on the Middle Ages. Most of the people at that time couldn't read or write, but a few learned men left behind them first-hand accounts of what their life was like. And a few public records are still available.

The paintings of the time were mainly religious, but their

12

creators told the dramatic stories of the Bible in terms of living, moving people. Naturally they painted a bit of the life they knew into their work.

From a study of paintings and tapestries, woven to hang on castle walls, from historical data and from legend come the impressions which make up a clear picture of medieval life.

1. THE CASTLE:
HOW NOBLEMEN LIVED

LARGE MEDIEVAL households

IN THE BACKGROUND OF SUCH A PAINTING or tapestry, there might be a castle—a large stone structure surrounded by walls and topped with towers. The castle might be built high up on a hill so it could be defended easily, or it might be encircled with a wide ditch, called a moat, which had to be crossed to reach its gates.

A castle was home to many people. Inside its walls, in a large central building of stone, lived a noble, his family and his knights. Servants and soldiers belonging to the noble lived outside in the courtyard or bailey, in a cluster of small wooden buildings. Here food was prepared, tools and arms were made and repaired. If the people who lived inside the castle walls wanted to go outside them, they crossed a drawbridge which was kept lowered by day, except in times of war.

Outside the castle walls lived peasants in their huts. If there was an attack, they protected themselves by fleeing over the drawbridge and inside. These peasants were known as serfs and they worked the noble's land.

To the people of the Middle Ages, such a way of life seemed the only sensible arrangement. It came about because of events that happened hundreds of years before, when the Roman Empire collapsed.

At the beginning of the fifth century, the Roman Empire ringed the entire Mediterranean Sea. Great cities with broad avenues and huge public buildings were part of the sprawling Empire, which included dozens of modern countries—from England to Egypt, from France to Turkey—and had its capital at the great city of Rome.

Such a far-flung Empire was difficult and expensive to govern. In time a series of wasteful rulers and many other economic problems beset the Empire and started it on its way to collapse.

During the fifth century Rome itself was invaded and sacked several times by bold fighting men from the North and in 600 A.D. Pope Gregory wrote of the ruined Roman Empire: "Everywhere we see mourning and hear groans. Cities are destroyed, strong places are cast down, the fields are depopulated and the land is become desert. . . . We see some led into bondage, others mutilated,

18

others slain . . . nay, what is become of that Rome that once seemed mistress of the world?"

Because of the situation in Rome, its soldiers were needed there. Without them, officials had no power, so there was no one to keep peace in the distant parts of the world which had belonged to the Empire. It was up to each man to protect himself and his home. In times like these, who can wonder that strong men chose to live in fortress-like castles?

LORÐS ANÐ VASSALS

The northern tribes that settled on the Roman lands in Europe were bands of fighters who followed one leader in battle. In return, the leader or chief supported his fighting men with what he took from the people he conquered. This system of personal loyalty to a chief was the basis for a way of living called feudalism, a word which comes from a Latin word meaning money or property.

Feudalism, or the feudal system, as it was often called, grew gradually. In the very beginning, each lord had his vassals, or followers, who lived in his castle as a kind of personal bodyguard. Maintaining his vassals was very expensive for the lord. So when his vassals wanted

19

lands and castles of their own, the lord was glad to assign holdings to them.

In the High Middle Ages, the feudal system worked like this. A great and powerful lord loaned to one of his noble followers a tract of land to plant and to use. The follower, or vassal, had to pay for the use of the land by furnishing fighting men when his lord needed them. He promised loyalty by kneeling and placing his hands between those of his lord. The vassal's chief service was to fight for his lord, but in peacetime he owed other services. Usually he attended his lord's court for a certain time each year. And he had to make a gift of money on special occasions such as the marriage of the lord's oldest daughter, or the coming of age of the lord's oldest son.

Even the greatest lords were vassals of the king, who was in theory the owner of all the land in the kingdom. The whole system was supposed to be an elaborate network leading to the king. But in practice, the king was very often at the mercy of his powerful vassals, who had their own armies and courts to compete with his.

A vassal inherited his right to use the land from his father, and in turn he passed it on to his oldest son. In time, noble families forgot that their land had originally been loaned to them by their lord. They held control over their enormous holdings and administered them as their own.

kNiGhTS

The nobles of the Middle Ages were knights. There were only a few knights not of noble birth, in fact. Knighthood grew out of the feudal system with its code of loyalty and common defense against roving enemies. Actually, knights were high-class fighters. They rode on great horses and wore armor.

The most common type of armor was chain mail— a strong, flexible and light-weight covering for the knight's body. This chain mail was made of thousands of small metal rings linked together or sewed on leather. Because it was relatively light, it could be put on and taken off easily. This was good protection against the sword or the lance. But when knights began to use great battle-axes and maces (a kind of club) the chain mail was not strong enough.

Then the knights took to wearing plate armor, or sheets of solid metal, on their arms and legs. And of course helmets were of plate. Gradually, in the late Middle Ages, knights began wearing entire suits of plate, often with a coat of mail underneath. Some of the finest specimens of plate armor on display in museums today are delicately hinged at the joints to give the wearer some freedom of movement. One of these suits of armor would fit a boy or a very small man today, for it was made especially for a knight of the Middle Ages when the average man was not much over five feet tall.

Horses wore armor too, and a knight on his horse was a fine sight galloping along on a sunny day, armor gleaming brightly. When he rode on a peaceful mission, the knight might open his visor, so he could see better and be a bit more comfortable. But if danger threatened, he closed his visor and looked out through small slits, so that his entire face was protected.

When a knight was completely covered up in such a fashion even his best friend could not recognize him. And in battle it was highly important to be able to tell friends from enemies. So each knight had a special design or symbol to identify him. This was his coat-of-arms. It might be an animal, a bird, or a geometrical design and it was painted on his shield and embroidered on his banner and on the surcoat which he sometimes wore over his armor. Since many of these coats-of-arms were colorful, a tournament where many knights gathered was a bright scene.

Warhorse, armor and the rest of a knight's necessities were worth a small fortune, so no one but a young man from a rich family could aspire to knighthood. But wealth alone was not enough. Every knight underwent strict training.

When a boy of a noble family was about seven years old, he was often sent away from home to be a page in the castle of another lord. In a large castle there were often several dozen pages ranging in age from seven to thirteen, so there were few dull moments. After a year or so, a page was assigned to one special lady, who taught him pleasant, graceful manners. He also learned to ride, to shoot, to sing and to accompany himself on the lute, which one might call the great-grandfather of the guitar. In some noble households, he might even be taught to read and write.

When he was about fourteen, a page became a squire, and he was assigned to a particular knight. It was now his duty to keep a high polish on his knight's armor, to care for his knight's horse, and to take his turn standing guard at the castle wall. His knight taught the squire how to use a knight's weapons—mostly the sword and the lance. When the knight rode off to battle, his squire rode just behind him to serve him and care for him in case he should be wounded.

At age twenty-one, the squire finished his training period. For a day and a night he touched no food. All night long he remained alone in the dark chapel, kneeling by his armor, and praying that he would be a strong knight and a gallant one. At dawn, when the household gathered, the new knight's sword was blessed by a priest, who prayed that it be used in defense of the church and of weaker folk who needed the protection of the strong. Next the young man placed his hands between those of his lord and swore to be a true knight. The lord struck him lightly on each shoulder and on the neck with his own sword, saying, "In the name of the Father, the Son, and the Holy Spirit, I dub thee knight."

Occasionally young men were made knights for some deed of valor in battle, but that was unusual, and most knights went through the customary training.

A young knight was supposed to be ready at any time to defend his lord, women and children, and the church. He kept in trim for real fighting by taking part in tournaments. These included contests between whole groups of knights. But jousting, the most exciting feature of such a tournament, was single combat between two knights. They charged straight at each other on horseback, armed with long blunt lances. The one who knocked the other off his horse was the winner. The victorious knight might ransom the defeated one; so a tournament was an opportunity for a knight to add to his finances as well as to his prestige.

These gay events, like sporting events today, were enormously popular with the people of the Middle Ages. Visiting knights camped near the field of combat. Heralds announced the names of the knights participating, and a trumpeter played a loud fanfare as the knight rode onto the field. Along the sides were pavilions where the ladies, the judges, and those nobles who were not in the tournament could sit and watch. Often a knight asked a noble lady if he could wear her colors and fight for her. With her scarf tied to his lance he would gallop into the mock battle.

Since war was really his business, however, a knight spent a great deal of time away from his home. He would ride off, armor gleaming, pennants flying. Sometimes he would fight for his lord. Or he might fight in a more general battle, such as a Crusade. His loved ones were left behind hoping he would return safely and soon.

The LaDy of The Castle   —A Story

NEAR THE WINDOW, WATCHING the large silent snowflakes falling through the air, sat Lady Alison. She was chilly in spite of the fur-lined cloak she wore, in spite of the cheery-looking fire crackling in the great hooded fireplace. The heavy stone walls and floor of her castle home breathed out dampness and cold. Her three ladies-in-waiting were cold too as they sat nearby, two of them working fine embroidery while the third read aloud from a French romance.

Young Adela, the only one of the four who could read easily, turned the pages of a hand-written manuscript. The story was about a Crusader who was about to leave his home to fight the Infidels in the Holy Land. As his lady pleaded with the knight not to leave her, Lady Alison jumped up and said, "Pray, stop, Adela! This puts me too much in mind of my own Robert's leave-taking. Let us have a game of chess instead."

As she approached the chessboard, which lay on a low table near the great fire, the old dog that had been dozing by the fire rose and nuzzled her hand. "Good Bess," Alison said, rubbing the hound's broad head and looking into her gentle eyes. "You understand. You miss Robert as much as I."

29

Bess had not been young when Robert left—now she was ten years old. But still she followed her mistress about with a question in her eyes.

As Adela set up the chessmen, she said, "My lady, God will protect and guide our lord Robert. Has he not gone to fight for the Holy Land? Surely God will take care of a Crusader."

"I pray you are right," Alison said. "All I know is that Robert has been gone these four years. And now Edward too!"

"Oh, my lady," said Adela, "you know well that a nine-year-old should begin his knightly training."

"Yes, and Duke William is a fine man. I am glad Edward could be a page in his household. But this winter has seemed overly long without my menfolk around me."

One of the other ladies chimed in. "It *has* been dull lately. What I would not give for a day's hunting in the fields with my falcon on my wrist and a good horse under me!"

"I—I should wish for a tourney," Adela said wistfully. "But without Count Robert it would be a sorry affair."

"Do you remember when he unhorsed Sir Philip?" Alison brightened at the thought. "I can still see the great lout toppled off his horse by Robert's lance, falling to the ground with a clatter."

30

Enid, one of Alison's ladies, had been standing near the window. Suddenly she interrupted, "Listen. There's some commotion in the court." She stood on tip-toe and peeked out.

Visitors were few at the castle, so everyone was vitally interested when the watchman's horn was blown. Now Enid made a place at the narrow window for Lady Alison and they watched the men running to the great towers that guarded the outer gate. They could hear faintly some voices and the clanking and rattle of iron as the huge gates swung slowly open. At that point, a young squire rushed into the great hall to announce to Alison and her ladies that the visitor was His Grace, Duke William.

The Duke was Robert's lord, and it was he who had taken Robert and Alison's young son Edward into his household. Now he was on a trip about his great holdings to pay friendly visits to his many vassals and to see how they were managing the land.

The Duke dismounted slowly from his big bay horse. The knights who rode with him joined him on the ground and after shaking snow from their cloaks, all entered the castle hall, where they were welcomed warmly by Lady Alison.

As they gathered about the big fire, Alison sat by

the Duke, her cheeks pink with excitement, her blue eyes bright and eager. First she asked the Duke about his lady and all of his household. Then she inquired, "And my lord, how is our Edward faring?"

Duke William laughed, "I was waiting for that! He is as bright and merry a page as ever we have had. Not only does he ride beautifully and shoot a straight arrow, but he has a sweet touch on the lute as well. And Father John says he is apt at his reading lessons. See—a bit of his handiwork!" He handed a small parcel to Alison. "Done on parchment with a quill, by himself."

"Pray excuse me while I read my son's message," Alison said. She broke the seal and read very slowly,

"Lady Alison from her son Edward—

G R E E T I N G .

All is well in the household of Duke William. My Latin is not very good, but my lute is better! Some day I shall come and sing to you. Send word of my father, I beg you.

Farewell, Edward."

"Ah, how good to hear from him," Lady Alison sighed. "Thank you, my lord, for this message and for the happiness of my son."

Duke William smiled. "It is I who should thank you for sending me a page who will one day become a great knight." Then his smile faded. "But what of his father? What shall I tell the boy? Have you heard any news?"

"Alas, no, my lord," said Alison.

"Then listen," said the Duke. He lowered his voice as he leaned toward Alison.

While they talked, the serfs set up the long oaken boards on trestles to make a table, and put on it huge tankards of ale, and bowls of a kind of stew made of salted meat chopped fine and mixed with barley and winter vegetables. Large chunks of bread were set out for sopping up the rich, highly spiced sauce of the stew. The implements on the table were spoons and knives. For dessert there would be cakes made of flour and honey, and apples and nuts.

But Lady Alison paid little attention to the preparations. Her face grew pale as she heard the Duke saying, "It is time, my lady, to proclaim Robert dead and to let me arrange a suitable marriage for you. You cannot manage these great estates alone."

"My lord!" Alison said. "Other women have done so! I have called Robert's vassals for fresh vows. I have seen to it that there is extra food in the larder in case of a bad harvest or a siege. I go myself on the rounds to see that the guard is alert, and the drawbridge drawn at night. And of course I have attended the sick serfs and have held court in my lord's place. We are ready for anything, my lord."

"Truly you are a gentle lady," said the Duke, "as well as a most loyal one. Very well, we shall wait another year; then I shall return again. In the meantime, think well on what I have said."

The Duke turned from Alison and attacked the stew with gusto. But Alison had little appetite now. She put most of her own dinner down on the rushes for old Bess, along with a huge bone that had been saved for the dog.

"Pardon the poor fare, my lord," she said. "To-morrow we shall have roast capon with almonds, and wine from France."

"Poor fare, indeed!" the Duke said, cleaning his bowl with his bread. "'Tis the simplest and the best, and excellently seasoned with spices from the East."

The shadows were growing long when the watchman's horn sounded again. Enid ran to the window.

"More visitors, my lady Alison," she said. "I believe they are minstrels! 'Twould be good to hear a merry song and a few tales this evening by the fire."

"Does it please you to let them in?" Alison asked the Duke.

34

"Yes, yes," he said. "Perhaps they bring news."

A squire led three minstrels into the darkening hall. In they trooped, their loose cloaks blowing in the wind, their instruments slung over their shoulders. They bowed low to the ladies, then stood before the fire, rubbing their cold hands.

"Where are you from?" Alison inquired of the nearest one.

"From France, my lady," he said, taking off his cloak and the loose hood that came to a point at the top. Beneath the cloak he wore a belted tunic of coarse blue wool and a short green shoulder cape cut into gay points. He had wrapped long strips of yellow cotton cloth about his legs to protect them from the cold.

"We have new ballads, new romances for you that will delight you. Never have you heard such minstrels as we."

Lady Alison laughed at the man's boasting. "That we shall discover for ourselves."

Bess was so fast asleep after her big dinner that she had not heard the minstrels come in. Suddenly the old brown dog jumped up, and the hair on her back rose. She growled deeply, then gave a piercing yelp, almost as if she were in pain. She shivered from head to tail as she threw herself upon one of the group—a tall bearded

35

man clad in a brown tunic and tight green stockings. She leapt up to lick his face, and whimpered with joy.

"Robert!" Alison whispered to herself. And as the man came to her side, "How the beard changes him!"

"Yes, my dear, it is I. It is Robert." He kissed her hand, then dropped to one knee before Duke William, who took Robert's hand in his own. Next Robert turned and put his arms around old Bess as she pawed him, her tail in a frenzy of wagging.

"My son," said the Duke in astonishment, for in truth he looked upon Robert as a son. Then he asked, "What do you in such low company?" as he glanced at Robert's companions.

Robert only laughed. "Low company, my lord!" he said. "These are none of your juggling and tumbling minstrels such as we know in England. These men are French troubadours who can sing for hours of the great Charlemagne, and they come here at my invitation to learn more of our own King Arthur and the search for the Holy Grail. In their own land they are welcomed everywhere and are given rich gifts by their noble patrons."

The squires came crowding in to welcome their lord, and the servants hurried to set food and drink for him.

Robert waved them aside. "We had food earlier, but

I for one am quite thirsty. What say you, my friends?"

Robert took a deep draught of ale from a tankard handed him by a page. Then he motioned to the page to give ale to the troubadours too.

He turned to Alison. "How fares our son Edward?" His very eyes seemed to smile when he heard that the boy was safe and happy in the household of the Duke.

It was a far gayer evening than any of the ladies could have expected that morning. Duke William seemed almost young with delight at Robert's return. As soon as Robert had quenched his thirst, Alison put into words the question all wanted to ask. "Tell us, my lord, how have you fared these four long years?"

Robert leaned back in his chair and took another sip of ale before he began his tale. Bess, her head on his knee, looked at him adoringly as if she understood his every word.

COUNT ROBERT'S TALE

WELL you know that four years ago this coming spring I set out from the port of Genoa with many other Crusaders. Finally we landed in the Holy Land—a hot dry land of pitiless sun, not easy for those of us from the misty green northern lands to endure.

One night, just after the men had drifted into sleep, some Saracens, as some people call our Moslem enemy, crept among us like spirits of the darkness. They either overpowered our guards or stole by them in silence.

I had just dropped off to sleep myself, my armor close to my head, my helmet beside me. Suddenly I was seized from behind in a cruel strangle hold, and dragged from our camp. Some of my men tried to rescue me, but they were far outnumbered by the enemy. And all I got for my own struggles was a painful gash in the leg. I found that six other knights had been captured too.

The enemy bound our hands and put us on camels, ordering us to silence. Then we set off across the desert to I knew not where. Those Moslems, to my surprise, were kind, always giving us water, whenever they drank themselves. Five times each day they spread their prayer rugs on the sand and faced toward Mecca to pray.

After a long hot trip, we finally reached a town. Its strange sights and sounds made a deep impression on me. We passed a street market full of bolts of silk from Asia, fine Egyptian linens, and beautiful gold and glasswork. My eyes feasted

39

on the market, but before they had their fill, we had passed it by.

At last we reached the end of our journey—a low building with a thick wall all around it. I was shown to a comfortable room where a slave gave me some loose-fitting perfumed linen garments. Another slave brought balm and bandages for my wound, which was still painful. As he left he said to me in French, "When you are well, my master will receive you."

What the balm was I do not know, but it gave me quick relief. Odd, isn't it, that these unbelievers should know secrets we Christians do not? They have herbs that cure diseases. They can carve wood to look like fine lace, and they have brought from the East a strange instrument that enables them to keep their ships sure and steady on their courses. It is called a "compass" and some say it is the work of the Devil, but I do not think so.

No matter how courteous my captors, I had no wish to remain with them. Despite my wound, I decided to try to escape that very night. In preparation I tore my linen coverlet into fine strips. Then I listened at the door of my chamber until I heard a guard approaching. Quickly I opened the door, sprang at him and covered his mouth with my hand so he could not call out. At the same time, I snatched his scimitar and held it to his breast. But I did not want to kill the man, so I struck him down with a blow of my fist.

Quietly I exchanged clothes with the unconscious guard and bound him with the linen I had prepared. Seeing no one,

40

I walked out of the palace into a lovely garden. From an orange tree I vaulted to some flowering vines on the wall. Before I knew it, I was on the other side and free. To this day I know not what happened to the other Christian captives.

Using the North Star as my guide, I set out in a direction I hoped was toward the sea. By night I traveled and by day I hid myself. My wound was troublesome at first, but it healed gradually.

When I came upon a small poor-looking inn one evening, I spoke the few Arabic words I had mastered, adding gestures to make myself understood. One suspicious fellow asked me where I came from. Ready for such a question, I made it known to him that I had traveled all the way from the land of the Turks. No one there, I assured him, would know my native language. And I made some nonsense sounds to prove it. All the people at the inn were satisfied with my story and gave me some food to eat there, besides a fine packet to take along with me.

At last I reached the sea, and saw a ship riding at anchor, shadowy in the darkness. I swam out and slipped aboard. For many days I kept myself concealed in the hold. Finally we reached port and I was amazed to find myself again in the Holy Land. After stealing ashore, I asked about for news of my fellow Crusaders with whom I had set sail originally, but could find no news of them. So when I located a ship bound for southern France, I boarded it eagerly, as the first stage of my homeward journey.

I arrived in France alone and penniless, without horse or armor, not even knowing the strange tongue of Provence, where I found myself. I knew I had little chance of convincing anyone I was an English lord, so I was feeling quite desolate when by chance I met these good troubadours, who spoke my own Norman French. I told them my story and they believed me. Luck was with me too in that they had heard some of our English romances and wanted to learn more of them. I assured them that if I might travel with them, they might visit England as my guests for as long as they wished, which would provide them the opportunity to become familiar with our ballads and lays.

As we traveled northward together, I was persuaded to try my hand on the lute, of which I have always been fond, as you know. And before long, I found myself singing some of my Norman songs for the lords and ladies of France. In every castle we were welcomed eagerly, for everyone liked our songs and stories, not to mention the news we collected as we traveled.

Now I am home again at last. In truth this is an occasion to celebrate.

As ROBERT FINISHED HIS TALE, HE turned to one of the troubadours. "Henri, give us a song or two."

Henri was the minstrel whose boasting had amused Lady Alison. He was jolly and only half-serious. In a laughing, mocking way he began a song telling of the sadness of love. He placed his lute on his lap and as the shadows flickered across the great hall sang . . .

"Singing, I ride
My art I can't hide
When my steed and I gallop along.
He twitches his ears
Whenever he hears
My voice raised aloft in a song.

Foul weather or fair
My song's in the air.
Oh, nothing can keep me from singing.
Lively with gladness
Or drooping with sadness
My voice in the air will be ringing.

Now were I a dame
Either lovely or plain
I'd seek minstrel with lute on his knee.
To sing of my beauty,
From love, not from duty—
Indeed, I'd seek one just like me!

But, ladies so fair,
Smooth-skinned, debonair,
Let my anguish now sadden your hearts.
My lady is proud.
She has not allowed
That she cares a small fig for my arts.

I've made many a song
Full sprightly and long.
I've called her a pearl and a dove.
Yet this fair sweet saint
Says "Isn't it quaint?"
Will she never take heed of my love?

Her pride was my goad
And I took to the road
To wander about near and far.
My only pleasure
Is to sing of that treasure
Far away as a bright winter star.

My ladies, sweet, pretty
Pray give me your pity
For my deathless love unrequited.
And just in passing
I don't mind asking
Don't you think that the lady's short-sighted?

When Henri had finished his song, the company applauded loudly and called for more. But Count Robert said, "My friends, there is much to do tomorrow. We all need sleep, so let us retire."

Lady Alison's smile was radiant as she held out her hand to Count Robert. Together they led the way from the great hall. The household serfs banked the fire and dragged their pallets close to the embers for the night.

The Crusades

COUNT ROBERT WAS A CRUSADER. THIS WORD comes from the Latin word for cross and it means a fighter in a religious or holy war.

Most of the good people of Europe who took part in the Crusades wanted only to conquer the Holy Land. This was Palestine, now Israel, where Jesus once lived. But this area was also sacred, for different reasons, to people of the Moslem faith. So they too wanted control of the Holy Land.

Many Moslems were nomad Arabs. These men had been traders for many centuries. They knew the long hard routes overland to India and China as well as to many closer lands.

The nomads had become followers of the prophet Mohammed in the seventh century A.D., and wherever they traveled, they took their religion with them.

As they journeyed, the Arabs gained knowledge in many different fields, for, though Europe had forgotten so much, civilization in the countries of Asia was advancing rapidly during the centuries after the fall of Rome. From the Greeks in Constantinople, now Istanbul, the Moslem or Mohammedan Arabs and Turks learned about the science and art of ancient Greece.

They translated the writings of the European Greeks into Arabic. So learned Arabs knew about the great Greek writers at a time when most of Europe had forgotten that the ancient Greeks ever lived.

The Moslems conquered parts of Spain and Sicily and introduced their knowledge of ancient Greek learning. Here the learned men of the Middle Ages rediscovered Aristotle and Plato. The few Europeans who could read and write and were eager for knowledge became familiar with these philosophers and with Arabic science long before the Crusades.

But the men who were exposed to Moslem culture in Palestine on the Crusades were not scholars, but fighters. The knights and the common folk accompanying them found much to intrigue and fascinate them in the Arab world. There were the beautifully polished curving steel swords so different from their own. And there were the fine silks and linens which the Moslems had found in China and India and Egypt. The Christians marveled at lush farms and orchards situated on the very edge of the desert.

At first Europeans were a little shocked to find Moslem doctors treating sickness and actually curing people. Most of them had believed that people got sick because it was the will of God, and it was much safer to do nothing about it.

During the Crusades, Christians came into direct contact with the Arab world and its learning. Some of them were introduced for the first time to the culture of the ancient world. They saw Arabic translations of great literature copied out on a wonderful new stuff called paper. They heard tales of learned Arabs who could figure out difficult mathematical problems with a system called algebra. And they found that the Arabs had a simple way of writing numbers, much different from the clumsy Roman method they used.

The Crusaders, few of whom had been far from their homes before, could not help comparing the way of life they encountered abroad with that which they knew in Europe. Some of them looked with longing at the rich cities of Egypt, of Asia, of Spain. They wanted for themselves the wonderful silks and porcelains of the East, the gold and the jewels. Perhaps most of all they wanted access to Eastern spices. At home they had no way to preserve their meat and often it was half-rotten. Spices would help preserve it and also disguise its strong flavor.

The only way that Europeans could get the things they wanted was to trade with the Moslems. For the Moslems eventually won control of all the overland trade routes to the East, to the faraway wonderlands of China and India. Some of the Crusaders wanted to own the trade routes themselves. So they were fighting not only for possession of the Holy Land, but for possession of trade routes.

The reasons behind the Crusades were complex, but like all wars, they cost a great deal of money and many lives. Thousands died in distant lands where they went to fight. But those Crusaders who returned to Europe brought back with them tales of other lands and other

50

cultures. There was new interest in learning and slowly but surely, Europeans regained their forgotten cultural heritage and were stimulated to move on to new ideas and original thought.

II. THE ABBEY: how churchmen lived

The powerful church

MEDIEVAL EUROPE UNDER THE FEUDAL SYS-
tem was a war-like place. But inside the abbeys, monasteries and convents of the Roman Catholic Church life
was orderly and serene. Many religious establishments
dotted the landscape in the Middle Ages, and the church-
men and churchwomen who inhabited them were directly
subject to the great Holy Father, or Pope, in Rome.
They lived by stringent rules which forbade fighting,
except in a holy cause, like a Crusade.

The little that was left of Roman learning was pre-
served in monasteries and abbeys. Monks copied books
and kept brief accounts of important happenings. They
wrote in Latin, the language of scholars, for they con-
sidered the spoken languages of Europe, like the people
who used them, crude and vulgar. The monks also taught

55

a few young people to read and write. For a long time, Europe's only schools were kept in monasteries.

The word "catholic" means general or universal, and the Catholic Church was just that for all the Christians of the Middle Ages, for they all belonged to one church. They were part of a great religious empire as extensive as the Roman Empire had once been. The dictates of the Church extended into many parts of their lives.

The knights, for instance, who were the trained fighters of the day, were taught by the Church to respect God and defend the Christian faith, to protect the poor and weak. It was the Pope who proclaimed the Truce of God, which forbade all fighting on Saturdays and Sundays.

Although knights would sometimes disregard the Church's commands, a powerful lord might force his vassals to obey them. In general, the nobles were willing to support the Church with money and gifts. They felt it held the keys to the kingdom of heaven and they also recognized the Church as a peaceful influence in their world.

The copyist —A STORY

WHEN COUNT ROBERT ARRIVED home he brought a small packet with him. In all the hustle and bustle of his homecoming, it was almost forgotten. But not quite. Shortly after he returned, he set out for the Abbey on his horse, carrying the mysterious packet.

The Abbey, a few miles from Robert's castle home, was a cluster of buildings grouped around a central courtyard. This was an estate almost as large as Robert's, with its own farms and fisheries and great vineyards. But this estate belonged to the Church. Father Paul was the Abbot, or ruler of the Abbey and all its lands.

The Abbey gate was opened to Robert quickly and eagerly. Everyone in the countryside had heard of his miraculous escape from the Infidels, and most of the monks of the Abbey had known him well before he left for the Crusade. So he was welcomed with "May the Lord be with you, Sir Robert!" and other greetings from all sides.

After he had returned the greetings and dismounted, he walked quickly into the beautiful Abbey church to say a prayer of thanksgiving for his safe return. As always, he took a deeper breath when he saw the interior of the church. To him the high, leaping arches, the strong tall columns were like a dream forest of trees with branches meeting far overhead. And the windows! Aglow with the morning sun, they cast their patterns of colored light inside the church. Rich ruby reds, blues, emerald greens and many other colors made the church a place of shimmering loveliness. It was like being inside a jewel, Robert thought.

The Abbey church, like most churches of the Middle Ages, had taken many years to build. It was now complete, except for one more stained glass window to be placed over the entrance door. It was old Father Paul's wish that this should be a rose window, a large scalloped circle, of which there were very few in England. Such a window would be costly, but Father Paul hoped to be able to install one in his lifetime, so that he could see the Abbey church completed at last.

Robert was praying. As he rose from his knees, he glanced to his right and saw Brother Louis, the copyist, his head bowed in prayer. Many times Robert had marvelled at the exquisite work Brother Louis did, the fine black letters and the glowing colors of the decorations, set off with gold leaf. He waited until Brother Louis finished his prayer. When their eyes met, Brother Louis' gentle face broke into a welcoming smile.

60

"Sir Robert!" he whispered.

"Come along with me, Brother Louis," Robert said. "I have a surprise for you and Father Paul."

Robert led the way to the cloister, or arched walk that went from one building to another. The courtyard was beautiful. Spring was coming and some of the bushes were beginning to bud. A willow in the corner was actually in leaf, its leaves golden with newness, precise and tiny. Robert walked to the far end of the cloister, to the door that led to the chambers of Father Paul. As he opened the door, he turned enthusiastically to Brother Louis who followed him. "You will be truly interested in what I have to show to you and Father Paul."

The old Abbot was speaking to a monk when Robert and Brother Louis appeared. But the minute he saw Robert, he dismissed the monk and hurried to greet his old friend. "God bless you, Robert," he said warmly.

Robert bowed low. Then he took the mysterious package he had brought to the Abbey from under his cloak and handed it to Father Paul. He watched as the Abbot unwrapped several layers of cloth. He watched as Brother Louis tiptoed closer. And he saw their faces light up with joy at a copy of "The Ethics" of Aristotle, the great Greek philosopher, in Latin.

"Aristotle!" said Father Paul, delightedly. "I saw a

copy of this great man's writings on a trip to Oxford, but I hardly dared hope that our own Abbey would ever be in possession of one. Wherever did you get it?" He turned a page and stopped to look closely at a large black capital letter.

"My friend Henri, the troubadour, bartered for it and got it at a bargain price in southern France. I am happy that it gives you so much pleasure."

Brother Louis said nothing, but he looked at the book with great interest while the other two talked. It seemed he could not take his eyes away from it.

"The book is my gift of thanksgiving to Mary, the Mother of God, for my safe return," Robert continued. Then he knelt and the old Abbot made the sign of the cross over him, blessing him.

At last Brother Louis turned from the precious volume to Father Paul. "My father, may I have your permission to copy the Aristotle?" When the Abbot assented, Brother Louis said a quick "God bless you, Sir Robert," before he hurried away with the book.

At his tall desk, Louis turned over in his hands the treasure Robert had given the Abbey. He felt the heavy leather covers lovingly, as if the book were something alive. He looked closely at the thick parchment pages. It was a good clear copy, but, in all humility, Brother

Louis knew that his writing was as good or better.

The manuscript was in clear black ink with large beautifully wrought capital letters. Brother Louis, as he looked carefully at the copy, decided he would "illuminate" his own text, even though most copies of Aristotle were done in plain black. He would decorate the great capital letters with tiny pictures of birds and flowers. Around the borders he would draw curling vines. Reds, blues, greens, and above all gold leaf would turn each page into a thing of beauty.

Louis could not begin his work now, as it was almost time to go to the church service that preceded the late morning dinner. He was tired, as he had been up since dawn. He was hungry, too, since there was no breakfast at the Abbey except for the sick ones who needed an extra meal to keep up their strength.

Brother Louis smoothed his long robe and hurried to the church. After the brief service the monks marched to the dining room where each one found his place at one of the long wooden benches that ran the length of the room. As they ate their simple dinner of fish, pease porridge, bread and ale, the room was quiet except for the sing-song of the monk who chanted in Latin from the works of one of the Church fathers. Talking was not forbidden, but it was not encouraged either.

Usually Brother Louis ate in silence, his eyes on his plate, content to listen to the reading. But today he was brimful of excitement and joy. He turned to his friend, Brother George, and whispered, "I have Aristotle to copy."

"What good fortune," George whispered back. "Where did it come from?"

"Count Robert brought it," Louis answered softly.

"I pray you let me read it some day," Brother George said. He was not a copyist like Louis, but was

in charge of the song school, where bright youngsters who sang in the chapel choir could come and learn without charge. Although he worked with books all day long, George had never seen a copy of Aristotle. What a treat it would be for him to read the one Louis was to copy!

At the end of the meal, the monks rose and sang grace before they marched out through the long arched walks of the cloister. Louis enjoyed moving in a quiet rhythm with the other black-robed monks along the arched walks. He enjoyed the rise and fall of their voices as they chanted.

Soon the monks separated to get back to their work. They did many kinds, for the monastery was as complete a unit as the castle. Some of the monks went to the carefully tended fields. The Abbey orchards were pruned and grafted so that the fruit was famous for size and sweetness. Other monks were artists in leatherwork or woodwork. Some were copyists, some teachers. Whatever their particular duties, all were busy from dawn until darkness.

Louis found his Aristotle where he had left it. He put out some pages of clear parchment, the fine sheepskin that he used to write on. He had heard of something called paper that was made of rags. Louis wanted nothing to do with it, even if it was cheaper than parchment. Why should a man work for a year over a book only to have it tear apart in a few years more?

Brother Louis made ready the black ink, the colored paints and the gold leaf. Then he sharpened a quill pen and settled down to a happy afternoon. He did not hurry. After the first large capital letter was completed, Brother Louis eyed it with satisfaction. The glowing colors reminded him of the stained glass windows of the church. In *his* work, which was for the glory of God, even as those windows were, Brother Louis would put the same jewel-like colors, the same painstaking care that the artists put into the church itself.

NEARLY A YEAR LATER, BROTHER Louis put the last colorful touch on his beloved manuscript. And it *was* beautiful, its illuminated pages alight with glowing colors and gold. As soon as it was dry enough to handle, Brother Louis took it carefully and made his way to Father Paul's chambers. He knew that the Abbot would be eager to see his work.

The copyist paused at the door of Father Paul's chambers when he saw that Duke William was with the Abbot, but the old monk beckoned him in. In silence

Louis handed his copy of the Aristotle to his superior.

Duke William leaned close to the Abbot and together they looked at Brother Louis' fine work.

How the Duke would have loved to own the beautiful manuscript! Though he read very little, he longed to pass a great library on to his sons. Already he had twenty-four volumes, painstakingly done as was this one. There were few lords in the countryside with so many.

Father Paul noticed the eager look in Duke William's eyes. The Duke was a real friend to the monks at the Abbey and had made them many gifts. So Father Paul placed the volume in the Duke's hands. "For you, my lord Duke," he said. "Or if you prefer, you may have the original, and this one may go into the Abbey library."

"It is a generous gift, but one I cannot refuse," said the Duke. "This one it will be, done by my friend Brother Louis." Now the glint in his eyes turned into a true sparkle. "And—and Father Paul—do I not know of something you wish for as much as I wished for that copy of Aristotle?"

The Abbot thought immediately of the rose window —the only window still to be placed in the Abbey church! The thing he wished most to have completed in his lifetime. But it was too great a gift. He could not ask

67

for it. So sincerely he said, "We give you the Aristotle freely."

Duke William laughed, and looked enormously pleased at the same time. "Then just as freely I shall have a rose window placed in the space above the door of the Abbey church."

Months later, when the window was finally in place, the church was beautifully complete. It would be difficult to say who was the happiest; Father Paul with the window, Duke William with his book, or Count Robert when he realized he had played a part in the completion of his beloved church. As for Brother Louis, he never looked at the glistening colors of the rose window without saying a special prayer of thanksgiving to God for his skill as a copyist.

III. THE TOWN: HOW COMMON PEOPLE LIVED

The peasants' Lot

OUTSIDE THE MONASTERIES OF THE CHURCH, where monks worked for the glory of God, fields were plowed and harvests were gathered by the peasants. A few of them were free men, but by far the greater number of workers were "serfs." The word serf comes from the same Latin word as "serve" and "servant." The serfs were not exactly slaves. A noble could not buy and sell them at will the way he could his cows, for instance. Yet the serfs were certainly not free. They belonged on the noble's land, just as his barns belonged there. If a noble sold a piece of land to his neighbor, the serfs went with the land, just as a barn would go with it.

The main duty of a serf was to help his fellows take care of the noble's broad fields. In addition, nobles allowed their serfs little strips of land to plant for themselves. On this they raised food for themselves and their families, and perhaps a little extra to sell.

The serfs farmed the land in a very primitive way. Most of them knew nothing about the scientific farming developed by the Egyptians and the Romans long before. During dry times, they prayed for rain, but that was as far as they went. They rarely used fertilizer. Of course the land was quickly worn out. The only way the serfs knew how to improve the land was to let some of it lie idle, or fallow, each year. One third of all the farm land in Europe lay idle in this way, to make it fit for use the next year. During feudal times, a short crop could mean a terrible famine. It would have been a great help to the people of Europe if they could have planted all of their farmland.

Although food was often in short supply, the nobles and their friends sometimes rode right through the serfs' fields on gay hunts. Of course the horses' hoofs tore up the delicate young plants and ruined the work of months. But the serfs rarely complained. It seemed to most of them that God meant the serfs to work and the lords to rule.

During times of war, when the ladies and the knights shut themselves up in their great fortress homes, the serfs suffered most. Early in the Middle Ages, especially

74

on the continent, the nobles fought about all sorts of minor grievances. If one noble insulted another, there was nothing to do but fight it out. The serfs would not have had it otherwise, for they were proud of their masters' bravery. All the same, it was the grain fields tended by the serfs that were burned off by enemy soldiers. The knights might ride out from the castle and beat off the soldiers, but by that time the damage was done. And the serfs, that summer, would have little left to eat in the ruined fields. So while the nobles thought of war as an exciting and honorable adventure, the serfs went to the little village churches and prayed, "Oh Lord, let us have peace."

Besides farming, the serfs, men and women alike, were expected to help in the castle and perform all sorts of jobs for their master, and had many taxes to pay him. They had little money, so they paid their taxes with their work, with a certain number of their chickens, or a pig or two, or a measure of flour.

Not all the nobles were harsh and cruel masters. Many were kind and generous. They gave their serfs good homes, and if there was a shortage of food, fed their serfs as much as they dared from their own supplies in the castle granary or storehouse.

Indeed, in the Middle Ages, as in most of history, it

is a serious mistake to try to separate opposing forces into the all good and the all bad. Historical developments are rarely that simple. The relationship of nobles and serfs had grown up over a period of centuries. No one could change it suddenly. Most people, nobles and serfs alike, assumed that this was the way society had to be organized, the strong protecting the weak in exchange for servitude. Heaven was above, hell below, and on earth things were the way God intended them to be.

When in time many nobles freed their serfs, the serfs either became independent farmers or moved to the new cities. In either case, they were free to come and go as they pleased.

How did this gradual freeing of the serfs come about? It was not because of a burst of good will on the part of the nobles of Europe. Several causes led to the change. Like all oppressed people the serfs dreamed of their freedom, and the bolder ones tried to seize it. Eventually there were peasant revolts all over Europe.

Besides, the nobles constantly needed money for their private wars and for the Crusades, because fine armies and prancing horses cost money. They often found that they made more money by collecting a yearly rent in money from free men working their land than by having to bother with all the pig-dues and chicken-dues and other taxes that the serfs had paid for so long. And they found that free men worked harder on the land than did a man bound to servitude, no matter how capable he might be. When a serf could raise a little money, his lord was often glad to let him buy his freedom.

After a terrible plague called the Black Death swept over Europe in the middle 1300's, killing almost a third of her people, workers were so scarce that they could ask for and get better terms.

The poorer people themselves sometimes took matters into their own hands. In England, for instance, a group of serfs and workers marched on London singing, "When Adam delved and Eve span, who was then the gentleman?" It took the serfs several centuries to win from the nobles the right to live where they pleased and to work for wages, which were theirs to use as they pleased.

Some of the more impatient ones simply ran off to the growing countries of eastern Europe, and to the towns that were springing up on the rivers and roads of every land.

John goes to the Town — a story

CLUMPING ALONG A ROAD IN HIS heavy shoes was John, the serf. He had on his best woolen tunic, his dark hair was neatly combed and his face freshly washed. This road on Count Robert's land was muddy, but John whistled as he walked along. The buds on the trees were ready to open into tiny leaves in the soft spring air. Ahead of him, John could see a low, small cottage with an overhanging thatched roof. He quickened his step, hurrying across the well-trodden yard. He knocked, then lifted the latch and entered, calling gaily, "Kate! Kate!"

The small dark room that John entered was the only one in the cottage. Most of the light came from a fire that burned on a hearth in the middle of the room. The smoke escaped through a hole in the roof, but on the way it blackened all of the walls with soot. Opposite the door was a "wind hole" or window. A little light came in there, but cold came in too, since it had no covering except wooden shutters.

On the dirt floor a baby was creeping, trying to catch a young pig that ran away squealing. Two hens clucked contentedly in the far corner. Kate and her father were laughing at the baby's efforts, and also guarding him

79

from the fire. Kate's mother was stirring a porridge that bubbled in the heavy iron pot set over the fire. The piece of precious fat bacon she had put in with the beans and onions filled the air of the small room with a tempting aroma. A long loaf of freshly baked brown bread, a piece of cheese and a pitcher of milk were already set out on the small wooden table. Sometimes Kate's family had rabbit or squirrel stew, but for the most part they had meat only on feast days.

Kate made room for John on the bench where she sat.

"Has your father spoken to Lady Alison yet?" asked John in a low tone as he sat down beside her.

Her smile faded as she answered him. "Yes, and I cannot leave. Lady Alison says she needs healthy girls right here."

At this news, all John's eagerness vanished. He wanted Kate to be his wife. To her parents he had come, bringing a leathern bottle of wine, and they had taken it. That meant that John was accepted. But he lived on the land of Sir Philip between Sir Robert's castle and the Abbey. Robert and Sir Philip had quarreled over their boundaries many a time.

Since both John and Kate were serfs, they were not free to move about without permission of the lords who owned the land they lived on. Lady Alison, who was

80

generally a kind mistress, saw no reason why she should lose a strong, attractive girl like Kate to Sir Philip, Robert's old enemy. So she replied to Kate's father's question rather crossly. "Find her a husband here or among the Abbey serfs."

John sat and stared into the fire. "If only we were free," he said suddenly.

"Our lot's not so bad, boy," said David, Kate's father. "Mark you, today's a saint's day and we have no work to do."

John sniffed. "A saint's day! What about the other days? What about keeping the moat clean, and lugging firewood and working on the lord's land while your own grain gets over-ripe? What about his right to hunt a fox across your fields and ruin a whole year's labor for the pleasure of a single afternoon?"

But David would not be convinced that he was not lucky. " 'Tis all fair and easy enough," he said. "I work two days a week on the Count's land. In September I pay my pork-due—only one out o' eight of my pigs. In October I pay my head-tax. At Christmas I pay chicken-due and grain-due. At Easter I give ten days to plow, sow and harrow the Count's land. True there's digging in the moat and such-like, but they're none so bad."

John retorted angrily, "You've forgotten about the tax

when you bake bread in the Count's oven—don't you give him one loaf of every six? And the tax when you grind your own flour at his mill! And the tax when you run your grapes through his winepress! And the tax when you have a quarrel! I tell you, those up at the castle would have no fine gowns and prancing horses if *we* didn't work for them! Yet we are all descended from one father and mother, Adam and Eve. I say a plague on Count Robert and his lady both! And I care not if it kills them!"

Horrified, David rose to his feet. "Young fool!" he shouted. "Don't you be talking like that in my house. What if you were heard? Where would *I* be without a strong knight to protect me? I have no fine armor or strong horses! Yes sir, the knights and priests are different from us and it's our duty to serve and obey them."

Kate crossed herself. She too disagreed with John. "It's sinful to talk so, John," she said. "Did not God make the world as He wished? I will obey my Lady Alison. May God forgive you for wishing for the plague —I cannot. Now go, and don't come back. My father is right and you—you are an evil boy with bad thoughts."

"As you wish, my lady fair," John said with a mocking bow. "You'll not be seeing me soon again!"

Out of sight of the cottage, John tramped along. This

82

time he did not whistle. He stalked in glum silence. But he could not help thinking of Kate and all the plans they had made together. Why, when the parish priest was teaching him his letters, and the kind old man was urging him to devote his life to learning as a monk, even then he had wanted to marry Kate. And now here he was, wanting to get as far away from her as possible.

"If only we were free!" he repeated aloud. At that a plan began to take shape slowly in his active mind. A man could go free if he could hide himself for a year and a day in a town. And right here was a sign saying it was only twenty miles to Newtown. "I am young and strong," he said to himself. "Perhaps I could apprentice myself to a carpenter or a shoemaker. Then one day I would be free, and maybe even rich later on."

He knew running away was a risky idea, for Sir Philip, his lord, could be a harsh man. "If I were caught, I might be put into the stocks or maybe even cast into the castle dungeon," he thought. Despite this, John knew he must strike out and try to reach Newtown.

In the cool spring air, he could walk fast. Almost at a run, he found his way beneath the trees. He kept away from the roads and by dawn, was within a few miles of the town. Tired and hungry as he was, he felt happy and strong as he thought of the new life ahead of him. In this town lived thousands of free people, trading and working with no overlord to forbid them to marry whom they pleased. Another year and another day, and he himself would be a free "bourgeois," or town-dweller. Swiftly he made his way across the wide orchards, now bright and beautiful with blossoms, that lay outside the city walls. He could see the soaring spires of the new cathedral and some gabled roofs rising above the sturdy wall.

John made his way to the main gate where people were jostling one another across the wooden drawbridge. In the daytime, people were free to come and go as they pleased, but at night the gate was shut and the drawbridge raised, to guard against attacks.

The scene almost took his breath away. So many people milling about, talking and shouting! So many houses packed together inside the walks! John crossed the drawbridge to the main square. From it streets ran in many directions. Houses, some as high as three and four stories, leaned together around the square. They were built on wooden frames, and the pattern of the wood showed through the plaster. John thought they looked very pretty indeed. In most of the houses, the upper stories projected beyond the first. This made the uppermost story especially light inside, and the overhang protected the outside entrance from bad weather.

84

On one side of the square, people were shouting their wares. When an old woman tried to sell him a rabbit pasty, John's mouth watered, but he had not a penny.

There was not a tree nor a blade of grass in sight in the cobbled square, but behind some of the houses, John could see touches of green. He felt frightened at the strangeness of the city until he remembered that many of its inhabitants had come here for the same reason as he—to make a living as a free man.

When he stopped a neat-looking young man and asked if he knew of Joseph the shoemaker, the youth replied, "I do not, but go down this street till you come to Shoe-makers' Lane. You will probably find him there."

John hurried down the crooked narrow street. Here it was gloomy even in the sunlight because the houses projected out so far that they almost met overhead. Still there was something pleasant and alive about the town. John felt a tingle of excitement. Plenty of places to hide, he noticed.

He found his cousin easily enough, where long lines of shoe signs creaked and swung above the doors of the little shops. Most of the signs had pictures of shoes on them, so that one need not read in order to know where to get one's feet fitted. Here on this little lane the shoe-makers of Newtown lived and worked.

86

Joseph, John's cousin, was delighted to see him. He brought bread and cheese and ale, and they sat down to eat.

"Yes, yes," he nodded eagerly as John told his story. "We can apprentice you to someone. Plenty of serfs hide out in Newtown—it is like looking for a needle in a haystack to find a man here. Just don't go out on holidays or in the marketplace—and get rid of those clothes—they shout aloud of the fields."

Joseph took John to his friend Henry Black (called so from his hair and eyes) who was looking for a bright young apprentice. Joseph told him that John was a smart lad who knew his letters and that he wanted to become a free man in Newtown.

Henry's black eyes twinkled as he said, "You will not be the first I have helped hide out for a year and a day!" Then the terms of John's service were arranged. He would serve Henry for seven years and promise to be obedient and hard-working. In return, Henry would feed and clothe him, give him a bed and a little pocket money. At the end of the seven years, John would be a day-worker, or journeyman, and he would receive wages. Seven years didn't seem like such a long time to John, especially in return for freedom and a trade. And Henry seemed a kindly and pleasant man.

Joseph left, and Henry took John upstairs to the attic where he would have a bed of his own. "Do not move out of this room, young man," Henry told John, "until I have some other clothes for you. You may rest here until dinner at noon. We eat later in town than in the country."

John lay down and fell asleep in a moment. He awoke with the smell of roasting chicken strong and delicious about him. He sat on the edge of his bed and stretched happily. Truly he was thankful to God for guiding him to this good man's home. Now he was resigned to losing Kate, for he had found in return something at least equally precious—his freedom.

Outside the town bells were ringing the noon hour in a dozen different keys, their strong voices dying away softly across the gabled rooftops. Pigeons rose and flapped their wings as the bells rang. To John they pealed a song of hope.

FROM SERF TO BOURGEOIS

IN TIME, THOUSANDS OF SERFS LIKE JOHN became free city-dwellers. They were proud of their bustling, progressive towns, and they had every reason to be. Anyone with skill and energy could get along there. Hundreds of free towns began to spring up all over Europe, many around a cathedral or a great fortress. Others arose where bridges were built over rivers, and along other important roadways. Some grew out of villages that were once a part of a lord's manor, or estate.

As Europe became more and more civilized, travel became safer and free people arrived in the towns, bringing with them new ideas and new needs. The towns became large enough and strong enough to achieve a large measure of independence.

Often a group of townsmen, called "bourgeois" or "burgesses" from the Latin word for town, went to see the lord and offered him money for a charter which said they were free men, and that the lord gave up all control over the town, except for some yearly dues paid in money rather than work. Many towns paid taxes directly to the king.

As always, nobles were short on ready cash, so a lord might eagerly accept the offer of the burgesses. Undoubtedly some lords at first thought that they could simply take a few armed knights and regain control of the town whenever they wanted to. But many towns took steps to prevent this sort of thing. They armed their own men, and built walls twenty or more feet thick to guard against an attack from a lord or from anyone else.

The Guilds

The guilds helped the town-dwellers, or burgesses, keep their towns orderly and peaceful. These guilds were associations of merchants and tradespeople. There was a separate guild for every sort of craft—an armorer's guild, a weaver's guild, a shoemaker's guild, and so on. The guilds were different from present-day unions. It was largely masters who belonged to guilds, and today only workers belong to unions.

The guilds grew very powerful and wealthy. They were good for business. Only the guild members of a town were allowed to trade there. This kept merchants from other towns from coming in and making money at the expense of the local tradespeople. The guild member whose product was not as fine as it should be might be expelled from his guild.

The guild also stood behind each individual member.

It protected him in his dealings with dishonest people. Suppose a noble refused to pay a bill for some very fancy shoes, for instance. What could one lone shoemaker do to force a powerful lord with a hundred armed knights at his command to pay him a few pounds? But the shoemaker's guild, through the merchants' guild, might hold up a loan that the noble needed until he paid the shoemaker.

There were also many other services the guild did its members. If a man fell sick, the guild took care of his wife and children until he was well.

To become a guild member, a young man first had to become an apprentice. An apprentice worked for nothing but his keep and a little spending money for a number of years, often seven. Then he became a journeyman. That does not mean that he traveled around, but that he worked by the day. The word comes from the French word for day.

A journeyman worked for wages, and he saved his money to enter a guild. But even with the necessary money, a man still had to show that his work was good enough for the guild to approve and to stand behind. To prove this, he made a "masterpiece" and submitted it to the guild. A masterpiece was simply a fine example of the tradesman's work, whatever it might be. Today the word is used largely in connection with art. But in the beginning, it meant a kind of final examination that a man passed in order to become a guild member. When the guild members passed this, the new member became

a "master" in his trade and could set up his own shop. This was a proud title—and what was more natural than that he should use it? "Master Shoemaker," "Master Weaver," "Master Smith"—all originally descriptive of a man's work—have long since become "Mister" Shoemaker, or Smith or Weaver.

The guilds were important to the business of the town, and they also provided fun for the townspeople. Everyone loved to go to the big square to watch the plays that the guilds put on every year. These were plays about the lives of saints or Biblical characters. At first, guild members acted in them, dressed in fancy costumes. But by the end of the thirteenth century, semi-professional actors appeared in the guild plays.

The stage was on wheels so that it could be moved easily. Though these plays were deeply religious or based directly upon Bible stories, they were not always solemn. One favorite subject was "Daniel in the Lion's Den." The lion would wear a great wooly mane and a fierce mask. He would growl so loudly and jump around so wildly that it was impossible not to laugh. And when he decided not to eat Daniel, he would stand up on his hind legs and put his front paws around Daniel's neck. People laughed until the tears came.

These free performances, presented by the guilds to entertain town-dwellers, were the first plays Europe had seen since ancient times.

The towns gave the peasants, or serfs, the chance to become free. The guilds safeguarded their rights as freemen, and stood between them and the feudal lords. And then there were the universities. At first some of the town-dwellers showed their interest in learning by gathering about religious scholars and teachers. Different groups of students banded together and many of the great universities of Europe grew up during the twelfth and thirteenth centuries.

In time, many townspeople became well-to-do and formed a prosperous new middle class. In its turn, this middle class became large and powerful. Its very existence inspired poor people to move up in the world. After all, the middle class was made up of men who had once been just like themselves. It was a better and freer life —a life well worth working for.

The End of the Middle Ages

THE MIDDLE AGES lasted approximately ten centuries. During that long, long period, life in Europe changed greatly, and moved out of chaos to an ordered civilization. Of course the Middle Ages did not end abruptly. The transition to modern times was a continuous process of growth.

The Middle Ages was the time of the organization and spread of Christianity. Many of the great Roman Catholic orders of monks were founded, and the Church itself grew great.

It is unfortunate that the deep religious feeling which produced the many magnificent cathedrals and abbeys which date from this period was often accompanied by complete religious intolerance. It was assumed that a ruler would force everyone subject to him to accept his religion. Seeds of the Protestant movement were present as early as the eleventh century but only much, much later did freedom of worship become an accepted part of Western culture.

97

Freedom to explain the world, from the movements of the planets to the beating of the human heart also had its beginnings in the Middle Ages. The revival of interest in learning led to the growth of universities and to the appearance of such daring souls as those who insisted on backing up scientific theories with experiment.

Modern trade, so vital a part of the world today, had its start in the Middle Ages, too. Beginning in Italy, commerce with the Moslems and the Eastern Empire created new demands and made buying and selling profitable. Trade brought about in-

creased contact with the Moslem civilization, which added to existing knowledge. Then, in 1270, a Venetian named Marco Polo set out for China with his father and his uncle and lived there for many years. His marvelous stories of life in the fabled empire of Kublai Khan heightened interest in the Far East and made people even more eager to get to the lands of the spices.

Though Marco Polo and other adventurous men went overland, it was a difficult trip at best. Mountains and deserts and hostile tribes were in the way. When the Moslems took Constantinople in 1453, all overland routes to the Orient were

closed to the Europeans. But they wanted more than ever the spices and silks and other luxuries of the East.

Since the oceans were still free, ships from various nations began to make more and more daring trips into the Atlantic. The terrible rumors about being swallowed by sea monsters or dropping off the edge of the earth proved false. When some venturesome seamen set out for Asia and found America on the way, the world was opened for exploration.

The nation, as we know it today, grew during the Middle Ages. At first almost all the philosophers of the time agreed that the ideal government was the universal state with the Pope or the Holy Roman Emperor at its head. But gradually the church grew weaker, the kings grew stronger, and were able to rule over the nobles.

The increasing power of the towns and the rapidly growing number of free tradesmen created a kind of new force. They could side with local lords or with the king, whichever they felt was best. In England, where the king became strong sooner than the kings on the continent, it was the combination of townspeople and nobles who eventually put limits to his power, though the nobles were the ones who actually forced the king to sign the Magna Carta, or Great Charter. This guaranteed that the king could not be above the law, and that he had to rule with the consent of some of the important people in the country.

The basis for many of our present-day civil rights was laid during the Middle Ages. In the middle of the twelfth century, the English King Henry II gathered together a group of lawyers to advise him in revising the laws. One of the reforms then made was the foundation of our modern trial by jury.

Representative government, so important in present-day democracies, also had its roots in the Middle Ages. In 1295 Edward I of England called together a group that is known today as the Model Parliament, which included members from the nobility, the Church and the towns. And in 1302 King Philip of France called together members of these same three groups. The kings had no notion of beginning democratic government. They simply wanted to be less dependent on the nobles. But this was the start of true representative government.

Gradually new ways of thinking, of living, took the place of many of the old ways. Though some of the old ways were colorful and beautiful, others were sharply discordant with newer ideas. The Middle Ages was a unique period in history because age-old custom existed alongside the progressive thought which led ultimately to a modern world.